Jarrold Seashore Life Series Book 2
Photographs and text by
Heather Angel, MSc, FIIP, FRPS

Seashore Life on Rocky Shores

Jarrold Colour Publications, Norwich

As rocky coasts are pounded by waves, they become eroded away. Rocky headlands are formed by hard rocks resisting this erosion, whereas softer rocks are worn down by wave action and weathered to form the particles which build up sand and shingle beaches. The colour of the rocks and the way in which they have been weathered, provide the individual characteristic landscape of each particular stretch of coastline. The type of rock also influences the habitats on the shore itself: whether there are rock pools and crevices large enough for hideaways, or boulders beneath which animals can crawl.

The twice-daily cycle of the tidal ebb and flow has a profound effect on the life of rocky shores. The drying action by sun and wind on exposed shores, is a major problem which faces all inter-tidal life – especially on rocky shores. Unlike inhabitants of sandy beaches, described in the companion book, rocky-shore animals generally cannot burrow. Instead, either they stay put on the rocks, often protected from drying by an outer covering; or they seek shelter by crawling into either a crevice or beneath damp seaweed or a boulder. Some animals remain submerged in rock pools, but these are not such congenial habitats as might first be supposed. Progressively lower levels down the shore are exposed for shorter periods, hence the number of species increase with the distance below the high-tide level.

During the twenty-four-hour day, most places in Britain have two high and two low tides. But since the relative positions of the earth, the moon and the sun change daily, the actual time of low or high water is not constant, nor is the tidal range. The biggest ranging tides are the *springs*, which alternate fortnightly throughout the year, with the small ranging *neap* tides. The most spectacular spring tides occur at the time of the spring and autumn equinoxes. As on sandy beaches, low water of the equinoctial spring tides provides an opportunity for looking at life in a zone which remains submerged for most of the year.

The seaweeds and animals of rocky shores are not scattered at random over the shore; instead they occur in distinct zones. Species which will tolerate long periods of exposure occur high up the shore, while delicate soft-bodied species occur either in damp places or low down the shore. The tidal level, however, is not the sole factor influencing zonation. The degree of exposure to wind and waves also affects the distribution of certain species. Above the high-tide mark, lichens encrust the rocks, sometimes providing a distinct band of orange, black or grey-green. Lichens are dual plants, made up from two different plants – an alga and a fungus – living intimately together. Since both partners gain from the other's presence, this is referred to as symbiosis, or a mutual co-existence.

The region above extreme high-water level of spring tides, is known as the splash zone. The extent of this zone is smaller on sheltered shores than on exposed coasts. When Cornish and Pembrokeshire coasts are subjected to strong gales, spray is whipped up the cliffs 30 m or more above the high-tide level. On such coasts, the upper limit of some lichens, small winkles (*Littorina neritoides*) and barnacles is extended several metres above the average high-tide level. Although it is confined to rocky shores, the small winkle is almost a terrestrial snail, for it can survive long periods of drying, extending into weeks or even months. But when it reproduces, it is dependent on the seas for the dispersal of its planktonic larvae. Other splash-zone inhabitants of shores which are not too exposed, are sea slaters and bristle-tails. Sea slaters resemble overgrown woodlice. They hide away in crevices during the day, emerging to feed at night – providing the moon is not shining too brightly. Bristle-tails are primitive wingless insects related to the silver fish and firebrats found indoors. Like them, they have three slender bristles on their tails.

Walking past the splash zone down a sheltered rocky shore, the dominant feature is the brown wracks which festoon the rocks. These provide both shelter and food for a host of inter-tidal animals. Similar to the lichens and barnacles, these seaweeds are often clearly zoned. Brown wracks form the main bulk of the seaweeds on the shore, but other kinds also exist. There are the primitive blue-green, the green and the red seaweeds. All seaweeds, not just green ones, contain chlorophyll, but the green colour is masked by other coloured pigments. Like flowering plants, seaweeds use the chlorophyll for manufacturing food in the presence of sunlight by the process of photosynthesis. Since sunlight is essential, turbid or polluted waters limit the depth to which seaweeds can live and grow. Some red seaweeds do occur on the shore, but many more live offshore in the sub-littoral zone. Some of the delicate forms are exceedingly beautiful when seen spread out underwater or mounted on to paper. Seaweed mounting was an art which flourished in Victorian times.

During low tide, the brown wracks form an effective moist blanket under which many animals seek shelter during their exposure. So, apart from the hard-shelled limpets, barnacles, dog whelks and mussels, which remain obviously exposed on bare rocks, most of the life of rocky shores is hidden away, and has to be searched out from beneath seaweeds or boulders or in rock pools. Any boulders which are turned over, should always be turned back again, otherwise the seaweeds growing on top and the animals encrusting the underside will soon die if their positions are reversed. In gulleys where the sea water continues to flow after the tide has fallen, the undersides of large boulders are richly encrusted with colourful growths. Although fixed and unable to move around, sessile sponges, sea firs, sea squirts, sea mats and calcareous tube worms are all animals which create water currents to draw in their food supply. They are all filter feeders, like the fan worms and cockles of sandy beaches.

Many mobile animals also chose to permanently or temporarily shelter beneath boulders. Here, they avoid becoming dried out or being swept away by the ebbing tide. Some animals such as the brittle stars – the slender-armed relatives of starfish – naturally shun sunlight, while many others hide away from predators. Active animals such as brittle stars, crabs and fish will soon crawl or swim away when their boulder is upturned, but less active cowries, sea slugs, starfish and green sea urchins will either remain in position or else crawl slowly away. Gulleys which retain some sea water throughout the low-water period, are places in which sub-littoral animals unable to withstand any exposure to air, and therefore not normally found on the shore, can penetrate and survive.

It is the rock pools which fascinate both young and old alike. In these natural aquaria, sea anemones continue to wave their tentacles, prawns to dart through water, and winkles, topshells and small hermit crabs to crawl over the bottom, long after the tide has fallen. However, very few rocky-shore inhabitants seek out pools as a permanent place of residence, and some – notably the acorn barnacle – prefer the bare rock to a pool. Small rock pools, especially in the upper and middle parts of the shore, can be subjected to extreme changes in the temperature and the salinity. On a hot summer's day, the water temperature can rise by as much as 10 °C, only to suddenly drop when the incoming tide flushes out the pool. Conversely, on a cold winter's night, the temperature of a pool can drop several degrees below that of the sea water. A heavy rainfall during low water will dilute the water in a pool. So it is in the lower and deeper pools on the shore that the biggest variety of animals and seaweeds are found, where the inhabitants are kept bathed with sea water, approximating to the temperature and salinity of the sea itself.

The common limpet and the beadlet sea anemone are two of only a few animals which are equally at home in or out of rock pools. The green snakelocks sea anemone cannot contract its tentacles, and so it seeks out pools or cracks where it can remain covered by water. Some animals, such as fish and crabs, migrate from one pool to another during high water, and so become stranded when the tide recedes. Providing there is a supply of food and suitable hiding-places, such as rocks, cracks or seaweed cover, fish may inhabit a pool for weeks. The common blenny or shanny, butterfish, gobies and rocklings are all fish which regularly live in pools.

Even rock crevices where the water drains away can provide a sheltered, damp place in which the animals can survive during low tide. Small cracks contain a specialised crevice fauna, which is small in size, whereas large crevices can be rich sites for many encrusting animals, such as sponges, sea squirts and sea anemones. Caves also provide damp, sheltered and shady habitats. Where the full force of the waves is broken by the rocks at the entrance, the incoming water carries in food without scouring the inside. The walls of such caves can be completely encrusted with red, cerise, yellow or green sea anemones. Caves with large entrances can be explored with a boat, while smaller caves can be entered on foot or by swimming. It is most important to determine beforehand the exact time of low water, so that there is no chance of becoming cut off by the incoming tide.

Several rocky-shore inhabitants are collected commercially as food, of which the best known are mussels and crabs. In most areas, edible crabs are caught offshore in baited pots or by diving. On some shores, however, crabs are caught by hand using hooked poles to prize them from their hideouts in crevices or from beneath boulders during the equinoctial spring tides. In Jersey, where large edible crabs are rarely caught, spiny spider crabs are eaten instead. A renowned shellfish also eaten in Jersey and Guernsey, is the ormer. Even the southern shores of Britain are too cold for this giant snail which lives beneath boulders low down the shore and offshore in the Channel Islands. The rounded shell has a neat row of breathing holes and the inside is lined with a mother-of-pearl layer. Still collected and sold in South Wales and Ireland is the edible seaweed laver. After washing in fresh water, laver is boiled until it is tender and forms 'laver bread'.

The majority of life exposed between the tide marks on rocky shores, is seen in its inactive phase: barnacles and mussels are closed up, limpets are clamped on to the rocks, and crabs rest beneath stones. They come to life as soon as they are covered by the sea. In order to show the way in which these animals move and feed underwater, several of the photographs in this book are of animals in aquaria.

On sheltered rocky shores, brown seaweeds abound. At the top of the shore, the first kind to become exposed is the channelled wrack. This picture shows the seaweed still wet and glistening shortly after the tide had fallen. After six or more hours exposure to sun and wind, the seaweed appears not only dry but also brittle and dark brown in colour. This wrack, therefore, provides little effective cover or shelter for animals, but it does provide a source of food for some upper-shore animals. The rough winkles with their cream, dirty green or orange-coloured shells, and the sea slater, both feed on channelled wrack.

Bladder wrack is a larger brown seaweed which grows in the middle region of the shore. It has paired bladders which buoy the plant up from the rocks when the tide rises. Living associated with this seaweed are the flat-topped winkles. The rounded shells – especially the yellow-green ones – closely resemble the seaweed bladders. Winkles with yellow, brown or black shells, are more conspicuous. When the tide recedes, the winkles crawl beneath the wrack where they will be in no danger of drying out. They also feed on bladder wrack and between March and October lay their egg capsules on it. Tiny shelled winkles hatch directly from the eggs without passing through a planktonic larval stage. So they do not have to search out a suitable place in which to feed and live.

2

1. **BLADDER WRACK** (*Fucus vesiculosus*). ×0·70
2. **CHANNELLED WRACK** (*Pelvetia canaliculata*). ×0·80

3. **SERRATED OR TOOTHED WRACK** (*Fucus serratus*) in a shallow pool. ×0·15

4. Long fronds of **SEA BELT** (*Laminaria saccharina*). ×0·10

5. Second year straps of **SEA THONG** (*Himanthalia oblongata*). ×0·2

Serrated or toothed wrack, which grows slightly lower down the shore than bladder wrack, has no bladders, but distinctly toothed margins instead. Swollen ends which develop on this and on other brown seaweeds, are not bladders, but the reproductive organs called receptacles. When they mature, small spots of orange or green mucus ooze out from tiny hollows as the seaweed dries out. The orange coloration is due to masses of microscopic male cells which become mixed with the green female cells by the incoming tide.

Sea thong is another brown seaweed which produces in its first year, a concave disc. From the centre of this button grow out the branching straps shown in the photograph, to 2 m or more in length. In the spring and early summer, the straps become covered with brown spots which are the reproductive parts.

The 2 m long straps of sea belt with their frilly margins, become exposed only at the bottom of the shore. This seaweed is also known as the poor-man's weather glass, because the straps become soft and limp before rain, or brittle during dry weather. Horses were supposed to be fond of sea belt, which when dry, becomes covered with a white substance which is sweet to taste. This type of sugar gives rise to the name sugar wrack. Sea belt seldom survives for more than three years, which is much shorter than most of the other large oarweeds.

6. **OARWEEDS** (*Laminaria digatata*). ×0·12

7. **BLUE-RAYED LIMPET** (*Patina pellucida*) feeding on oarweed stipe. ×1

8. *Spirorbis borealis* tubes on **BLADDER WRACK**. ×3·5

6

7

8

During low water of the equinoctial spring tides, the upper fringe of the underwater oarweed forests become exposed for a short period. These spectacular brown seaweeds each have a glossy blade which looks as though it has been slashed into segments by a razor, growing out from the end of a thick stipe or stalk. The seaweeds are attached to rocks by a branching holdfast, inside which many small animals shelter. Oarweeds are perennial plants which grow out from the base of the blade in the spring and eventually the old blades become cast off. As shown here, red seaweeds grow on the stipes of old oarweeds. Plants which grow on other plants without gaining any nourishment from them, are known as epiphytes.

Living associated with all parts of the oarweeds is the small blue-rayed limpet. This picture shows one which has been feeding on the stipe. Oarweed stalks are naturally very pliable so that they can withstand buffeting by the waves, but once the outer layer is damaged or cut, the stipe is easily broken in two. The blue-rayed limpet can, therefore, cause extensive damage to oarweed beds, not so much by feeding voraciously, as causing the stalks to break in rough seas. Tiny white coiled tubes on seaweeds or rocks are the homes of tube worms which emerge to feed when covered by water (see also Plate 25). These *Spirorbis* worms are hermaphrodite and they fertilise their own eggs.

Living attached to seaweeds, especially those in rock pools low down the shore, grow fine, often straw-coloured, plant-like growths called hydroids. These are marine relatives of the fresh-water *Hydra* of textbook fame. Marine hydroids or sea firs, consist of a branching network from which many polyps, each with their own crown of tentacles, extend to feed and when disturbed or exposed, withdraw into protective cups. Larger hydroids which become washed ashore in tufts, are collected and sold as 'white weed', which is dried and stained for decorative use. When marine hydroids reproduce, they bud off tiny jellyfish which produce planktonic larvae. These larvae do not settle until they find a suitable site to metamorphose and grow into a new colony.

The star sea squirt which also grows on seaweeds, as well as rocks, forms exquisite patterns. This colonial sea squirt consists of many individuals arranged in a radiating star pattern.

As the name suggests, the chameleon prawn is a master of disguise. It is able to change its colour to blend in with its surrounding seaweeds. The one shown here crawling over sea lettuce is precisely the same bright translucent green, and yet when it was transferred to some red seaweed it slowly turned red. Changing colour uses up energy, so by night, it reverts to a transparent blue to conserve energy.

9. **A FEATHER HYDROID** (*Aglaophenia pluma*) growing on seaweed. ×2
10. **CHAMELEON PRAWN** (*Hippolyte varians*) on sea lettuce. ×2
11. **STAR SEA SQUIRT** (*Botryllus schlosseri*). ×2·5

10

11

12

13

12. **COMMON LIMPETS** (*Patella vulgata*) with old scars. ×0·5

13. **COMMON LIMPETS** (*Patella vulgata*) surrounded by serrated wrack. ×0·25

14. **DOG WHELKS** (*Nucella lapillus*). ×0·3

Limpets are one of the most conspicuous molluscs of both exposed and sheltered rocky shores. Both the conical-shaped shell and the large muscular foot, enable the limpet to withstand constant buffeting by waves. Any slight pressure on the shell will induce the limpet to grip the rock all the harder. A limpet can never be dislodged by gently tapping its shell; whereas a sudden sharp blow may catch it unawares. By repeatedly clamping and twisting its shell on to the rock, a limpet either wears a scar in soft rock, or else the shell itself becomes worn to fit the contours of hard rock. In either case, there is only one place where a particular limpet makes a perfect fit with the rock, and this is its 'home'. When submerged, limpets crawl over the rock rasping at a film of microscopic algae and tiny seaweed sporelings with a long toothed ribbon known as a radula. Limpets will continue to feed when exposed, providing they are in the shade and cannot dry out. By feeding on the young stages, limpets inhibit the growth of seaweeds on the adjacent rock (13).

Dog whelks live alongside barnacles, mussels and limpets. These carnivorous snails feed on mussels by boring through their shell, and on barnacles by smothering them with their foot. Dog whelks breed *en masse*, each female laying up to 200 yellow vase-shaped egg capsules in a year. The sting winkle – a pest of oyster beds – also lays yellow egg capsules, which are attached to rocks.

14

In estuaries, and other waters with plenty of suspended food, mussels flourish to form extensive beds. They anchor themselves to rocks, piers, buoys and vessels by radiating threads produced as a thick fluid which hardens in sea water. By shortening and lengthening these threads, mussels can adjust their position. The planktonic larval stages enable mussels to disperse into new regions, and thereby settle on the bottom of ships or inside pipes carrying cooling water to power stations. Settlement of mussels and other marine animals is controlled by bubbling chlorine through water. Mussel beds of commercial value occur in the Wash, Conway Bay and Morecambe Bay. The close-up photograph of mussels in an aquarium, shows the pair of siphons projecting between the two open valves. Water carrying the plant plankton food, is drawn in through the larger frilly edged siphon. Large orange gills strain off the food particles which are carried with mucus to the mouth. The waste is ejected in the current passing out through the smaller plain siphon.

Only after their larval stages had been discovered, was it clear that acorn barnacles are crustaceans and not molluscs as originally thought. Once the last larval stages have cemented themselves down, barnacles remain fixed for life. They feed by combing the water with their feathery appendages on their legs called cirri. When exposed, barnacles draw in their cirri and close down the upper plates.

16

17

15. Tightly packed bed of **MUSSELS** (*Mytilus edulis*). ×0·5

16. **MUSSELS** (*Mytilus edulis*) open underwater. ×1·5

17. Exposed **ACORN BARNACLES** (*Balanus balanoides*). ×4

18. **EDIBLE WINKLES** (*Littorina littorea*). ×0·5

19. **TOPSHELLS** (*Gibbula pennanti*). ×1

20. **PAINTED TOPSHELL** (*Calliostoma zizyphinum*). ×1·5

18

19

Most of the molluscs on rocky shores are snail-like gastropods, such as winkles, topshells and whelks. The common or edible winkle is the largest of the four species found on the shore. The shell is usually blackish brown, but it often dries out as a buff colour. When the mollusc withdraws into its shell, the opening becomes sealed with a horny disc, known as an operculum. Large numbers of edible winkles congregate together in exposed cracks and gulleys, where they are easily collected for food. Edible winkles spawn during the spring from February to April, usually at night on the flood tide. Each egg capsule contains three eggs which hatch into planktonic larvae.

Topshells superficially resemble winkles, but in the centre on the underside of the shell, there is a distinct depression called an umbilicus. The top part of the shell is often worn away to reveal the underlying mother-of-pearl layer. Grey, purple and thick topshells all live on the shore; but the largest and most handsome species is the painted topshell. The sharply pointed pinkish shell with its darker pink streaks is unmistakable. This topshell can be found in crevices, or beneath boulders and rocky overhangs low down on the shore. The above picture shows a painted topshell crawling underwater over a rock encrusted with a yellow star sea squirt. Compare the colour of this star sea squirt with the one in Plate 11.

The empty shells of cowries are more often found than the live molluscs, which live in cracks and beneath boulders low down on the shore. Although the two British species illustrated here are small compared with the tropical coral reef cowries, they are none the less interesting. When disturbed, the cowrie withdraws into its shell through the slit on the underside; when underwater, it emerges and crawls on its foot with outstretched tentacles. Thin skinfolds also extend up over the shell. These are mottled and therefore camouflage the shell, but if the cowrie is attacked, they suddenly fold back to expose the light shell. A second line of defence is an acid secretion.

Sea slugs also hide away beneath boulders. Some are exquisite colours and when seen moving underwater with outstretched tentacles, they are infinitely more beautiful than terrestrial slugs. These sea lemons were exposed to the air, and so they have withdrawn the pair of tentacles at the front and the frilly gills at the back. Many sea slugs are masters of camouflage: for instance, red ones live and feed on red sponges. Even these sea lemons blend in quite well with some of the colour forms of the breadcrumb sponge on which they feed. Sponges are primitive animals which filter feed when submerged. None of the British species resemble the bath sponge, which lives in warmer water.

21. **COWRIES** (*Trivia arctica* and *Trivia monacha*). ×3

22. **BREADCRUMB SPONGE** (*Halichondria panicea*). ×1

23. **SEA LEMONS** (*Archidoris pseudoargus*) with their spawn ribbons. ×0·5

22

23

25

24. **CUSHION STARLETS** (*Asterina gibbosa*). ×1

25. **KEELWORMS** (*Pomatoceros triqueter*) feeding underwater. ×4

26. Contracted **BEADLET SEA ANEMONES** (*Actinia equina*). ×0·5

The cushion starlet is the smallest British starfish. It lives beneath boulders and rocky overhangs on the south and west coasts. Like the larger orange starfish, it has five arms. Suckered tube feet emerge from the underside of these arms and enable starfish to crawl over and cling on to rocks at any angle. If a starfish loses an arm, it can regrow a new one – often starfish can be found with one or two arms missing.

Irregular white lines encrusting stones, small boulders and old shells, are in fact limy tubes made by keelworms. When exposed, the worms withdraw into their tubes, but when submerged they open out a fan of feathery tentacles, which withdraws again at the slightest disturbance. A magnifying glass is needed to see the beauty of the tentacles, which are used for sieving food from the water. A closer look will also reveal the characteristic triangular-shaped tube with its distinct central keel.

Beadlet anemones are the most widespread of all our sea anemones. Usually red wine in colour, they are also green or brown, but they always have a ring of blue spots around the base of the tentacles. When the anemones are exposed, the tentacles are withdrawn inside and they contract down into a blob of jelly; but underwater they become completely transformed, as the tentacles slowly open and stretch outwards (page 29).

27. **SHORE CRAB** (*Carcinus maenas*). ×0·6

28. **EDIBLE CRAB** (*Cancer pagurus*). ×0·3

29. Female **DEVIL CRAB** (*Macropipus puber*) in berry. ×0·75

27

28

Crabs of all shapes and sizes inhabit rocky shores, hiding away during low water. They have ten legs – a pair of pincers and four pairs of walking legs. The safest way to pick up any crab is by the back of the carapace or shell, where the pincers cannot reach. Having a hard outer skeleton, crabs can grow only by shedding this at intervals. They walk backwards from their old shell through a split along the back edge. After crabs have moulted, their new larger shells are soft and therefore vulnerable to attack by predators, as well as by fishermen who use them as bait. So soft crabs seek refuge for a few days, until their shells harden.

The tail flap, which is tucked beneath the body, is broader in female crabs, which use it to carry their eggs until they hatch into planktonic larvae. When crabs are carrying eggs they are known as being 'in berry'. The greenish shore crab, with its three blunt teeth between the eyes and five sharp teeth on either side, is abundant everywhere – including estuaries. The pinky-brown edible crab, on the other hand, is more at home in deeper water offshore, although young crabs do live between the tides. The devil crab – also known as a fiddler crab – has its back pair of legs flattened into paddles for swimming. This handsome crab is quite common beneath seaweed and rocks between the tide marks. Both the shell and the legs are covered with a felt-like covering of brown hairs.

30

31

30. A Pembrokeshire rock pool. ×0·3

31. A live **PRAWN** (*Palaemon serratus*). ×1

32. **SPINY STARFISH** (*Marthasterias glacialis*) with limpet. ×1

A cross-section of life can be seen in shallow rock pools low down the shore. The photograph on the left shows part of such a pool in Pembrokeshire. The lower edge is bordered by acorn barnacles, which do not penetrate into pools. The floor is lined with attractive pink encrusting and tufted seaweeds. Amongst these are limpets, edible winkles, topshells and beadlet sea anemones. Prawns also turn up in rock pools – especially in summer – where they become stranded by the outgoing tide. When disturbed they readily dart backwards away under cover of seaweeds. They can also move forwards by walking on their last three pairs of legs or by swimming using the paired flaps beneath the abdomen. The translucent body is marked with irregular purplish lines; but when boiled, it turns uniformly bright pink. Prawns are scavengers which use their two pairs of pincers for picking up pieces of food. Like crabs, female prawns also carry their eggs on their undersides.

Starfish also get stranded in rock pools. Spiny starfish will grow to reach a third of a metre across their diameter; so this specimen is quite small, as indicated by the limpet alongside providing a useful comparative scale. The spiny grey or green arms, marked with purple, easily break off at their base. The blood starfish, *Henricia*, and the sun-star only rarely become washed ashore. Both are bright red, but the sun-star has a variable number of arms, up to thirteen.

The distinct radial symmetry of open sea anemones does suggest a flower-like appearance; but they are animals which use their tentacles for capturing live food. Snakelocks anemones with green or brownish tentacles tipped with purple, frequent pools and gulleys. Because they cannot contract their tentacles, they must remain submerged, or at least keep moist, in a shady position during low water. In open sunny pools, these anemones are coloured bright green by large numbers of microscopic plants or algae living inside their tissues. This intimate association is known as symbiosis, both partners gaining from the other's presence: the plant cells gain protection as well as substances – including carbon dioxide – for building up organic food compounds, while the sea anemone has its waste products removed.

The dahlia anemone is the largest inter-tidal species. When contracted, it is difficult to spot, since the sticky outside is usually disguised with gravel and shell fragments. But an open dahlia anemone with its thick red and white tentacles, is unlikely to pass unnoticed. Compare the picture of a beadlet shown here with a captured prawn, with the one of many exposed anemones on page 23. Stinging cells inside the tentacles are used to stun or kill the prey. Sea anemones reproduce by fertilised eggs hatching into tiny planktonic larvae. Beadlets brood young throughout the year, especially during winter.

33

34

35

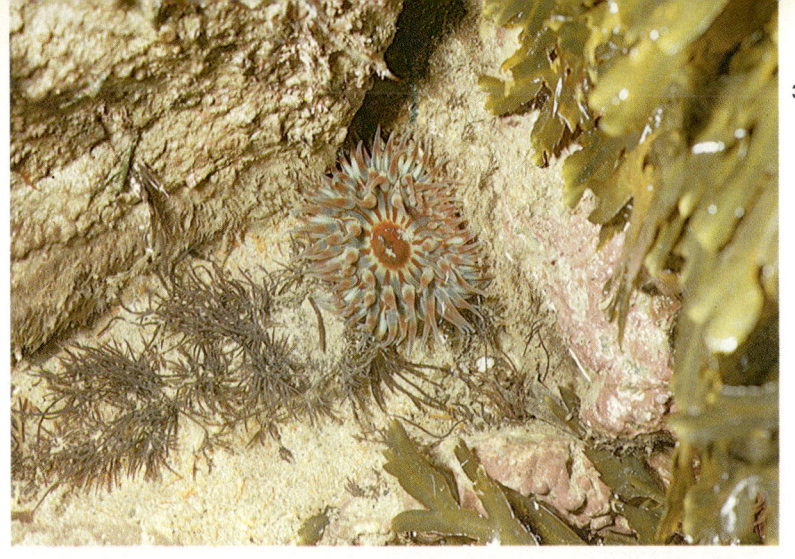

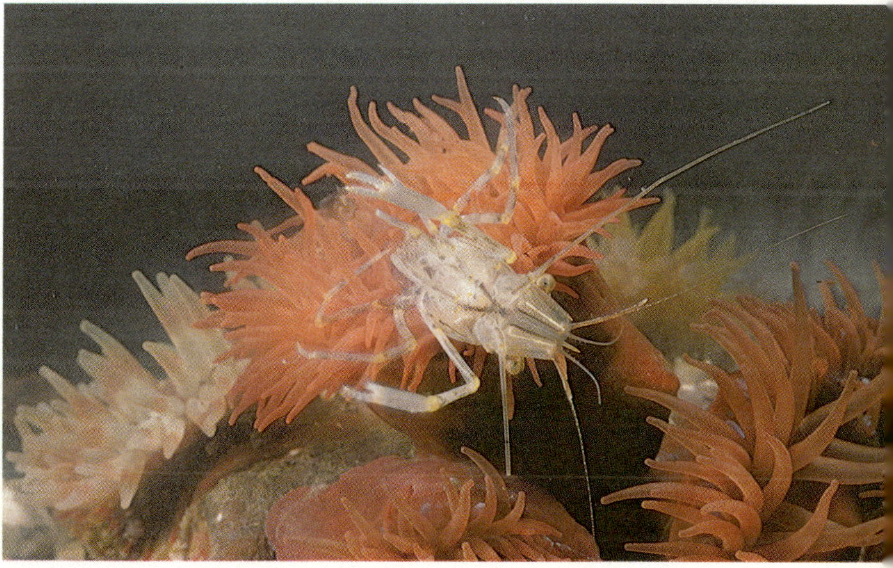

33. **SNAKELOCKS ANEMONES** (*Anemonia sulcata*) in a pool. ×1

34. Open **DAHLIA SEA ANEMONE** (*Tealia felina*). ×0·4

35. **BEADLET SEA ANEMONE** (*Actinia equina*) feeding on a prawn. ×1

36. **DEVIL OR FIDDLER CRAB** (*Macropipus puber*) head-on. ×1

37. **HERMIT CRAB** (*Pagurus bernhardus*) in a whelk shell. ×1·5

38. Underside of **GREEN URCHIN** (*Psammechinus miliaris*). ×3

36

37

The photograph of a devil crab in an aquarium shows its beady red eyes and distinct purple leg markings. This is a particularly aggressive crab, which can give a very nasty nip with its toothed pincers.

Hermit crabs use empty snail shells as their homes: small crabs live in winkle shells and at each successive moult they have to find progressively larger shells. Large hermit crabs, like this one, use common whelk shells, often encrusted with barnacles. Only the limbs which emerge from the shell for walking and feeding are hardened. The abdomen remains soft and anchors the crab by curling around the inner shell spiral. When danger threatens, a hermit can retreat into its shell, closing the opening with its enlarged right pincer.

Sea urchins are related to starfish, and like them, they have many suckered tube feet for clinging on to rocks. These tube feet are arranged in five double rows which run from the upper surface round to the mouth, with its five teeth, on the underside. When a sea urchin dies, the spines drop away from the underlying shell, revealing the rounded knobs which are the base of the ball and socket joint. This connection allows the spines to be moved. Tiny rows of holes in the shell mark the positions where the tube feet connected with the inside. The teeth are used for rasping at young seaweeds.

39. CORAL WEED (*Corallina officinalis*) in a rock pool. ×1

39

The pink, tufted branches of coral weed are so heavily impregnated with lime, or calcium carbonate, that they easily fragment. This, and other calcareous seaweeds, used to be classified with corals, which are animals, and it was not until the middle of the last century that they were recognized to be seaweeds. They live in arctic, temperate and tropical waters and they preserve well as fossils. It is now known that many so-called 'coral islands' have been built up mostly of fossilised tropical coralline seaweeds. This coral weed will not survive becoming dried up.